RESOURCE BANK

KU-376-318

LIGHT AND SOUND

CONTENTS

About this book

This book will help you to teach 'Light and sound' to Key Stage 2 (Primary 4–7) children by using examples from everyday life (for example, the use of light and sound by traffic on the road). The activities are designed to help you explore how light and sound travel from a source to a detector, such as a human eye or ear. Where possible, our everyday surroundings are used as teaching aids.

Included in the centre of this book is a double-sided poster. Both sides provide whole-class teaching tools. The full-colour A1 picture shows a child's view from the rear seat of a car, looking onto the scene of a fire; many familiar sources of light and sound are visible in the picture. The reverse of the poster shows the scientific vocabulary the children will need to use as they work through the activities in this book.

The book is divided into two main sections: 'Light' and 'Sound'. The themes covered include: sources of light; how our eyes work; reflected light; investigating shadows; sources of sound; hearing; how musical instruments produce different sounds; noise in our environment. In each sub-section (see 'Contents') there are a number of whole-class or group activities. Each activity has a specific learning objective; the ideas are developed and reinforced through a combination of small-group experimental work and whole-class discussion.

The content of the UK curricula relating to light and sound for this age group is fully addressed: the relevant parts of the Key Stage 2 programme of study for 'Physical processes' within the National Curriculum for England and Wales and the Northern Ireland Curriculum; and those of the Scottish Guidelines for Environmental Studies 5–14 under the Attainment Outcome 'Understanding Energy and Forces' for Primary 4–7 (Levels C–E).

INTRODUCTION

About light and sound

This book will help you to develop children's understanding of how light or sound is made by a source and detected by our eyes or ears, either directly or following interaction with other objects. In many cases, this is done by using examples that will be familiar to the children either from direct experience or from communications media such as television and computers.

It is worth noting that the National Curriculum for England and Wales and the Northern Ireland Curriculum both focus on the travel and detection of light and the generation and travel of sound from a vibrating source. However, the Scottish Guidelines highlight light and sound as forms of energy. Both light and sound are forms of **kinetic** (movement) energy: they are released during the conversion of energy from one form (such as electricity) to another at a source, and travel through the environment where they are detected. Light can also be classified as **radiant** energy: it can travel without a medium for conduction.

While all the curricula specify that children in this age group should have some experience of shadows and reflection, the Scottish Guidelines require that children should have a wider experience of light including coloured light and the use of lenses. Various aspects of the topic are addressed in this book. It has been left for you to decide which activities will be most appropriate to your class and curriculum, and where further development of the activities may be desirable (for example, trying the reflection activities with curved mirrors).

Common misconceptions

Children frequently come to believe that they observe objects around them because light from their eyes travels to the object and back again. Children may also find the idea of sound being made by a vibrating object difficult, because their primary source of sound is other people – who do not appear to vibrate! (The vibration of the vocal chords is not visible.)

Gaining confidence

After completing the activities in this book, the children should be able to state with confidence:
◆ that light comes from a source, and travels from the source to the detector;
◆ that light may pass through transparent materials, but not through opaque materials;
◆ that where light is blocked by an opaque material, a shadow forms;

◆ that light is reflected to some extent by all but black surfaces, but is reflected more effectively by shiny surfaces;
◆ that sound is made by vibration;
◆ that a musical instrument can produce different notes because the vibrations made by the instrument can be changed;
◆ that 'noise' in our environment is unwanted sound.
On completion of the relevant activities, the children should be well prepared to deal with this topic in their end of Key Stage 2 tests under the National Curriculum for England and Wales, or have a confident grasp of the relevant content of the Key Stage 2 Northern Ireland Curriculum or the Scottish Guidelines for P4–7, Levels C–E.

Safety

The children must be told **never** to look at the sun either directly or by reflection, and **never** to reflect it at somebody else using a mirror. Looking at the sun can cause permanent damage to the eyes.

Preparing to use the poster

The A1 colour poster must be displayed at an appropriate height to be easily accessible to the children (probably at the front of the room below the board), particularly for interactive work. Make sure that all the children are able to see the poster clearly.

On the reverse of the poster is a list of vocabulary that the children will need to use during their work on this topic. These words could be photocopied, mounted and laminated in order to be used as 'flash cards'; these will be a useful resource for development, consolidation and revision of the children's science vocabulary throughout. They will be especially useful

for supporting children who have difficulty in understanding and using the relevant terms.

Other uses for the poster

As well as being used for structured work on the topic of light and sound, the poster can be used to stimulate discussion relating to:

◆ sorting materials (either by functions or by physical properties);

◆ shapes and structures (in the context of maths, science or technology);

◆ identifying living and non-living things.

LET'S LOOK AT THE POSTER

GROUP SIZE AND ORGANIZATION
Whole class, sitting in a semicircle around the poster.
DURATION
About 20 minutes.
LEARNING OBJECTIVE
To become familiar with the content of the poster.

YOU WILL NEED
The 'car' poster, displayed where it can be seen easily by all the children.

DISCUSSION QUESTIONS
Look at the poster with the children. Ask them: *Where would you be if you could see this view in front of you?* The children should be able to say that they would be in a car, going somewhere.

Discuss with the children what they can see from this car. This could be done through a brief game of 'I spy'. Bring out their experiences of being in a storm, including the sudden change from sunshine to being under a thunder cloud (to stress the point that darkness is an absence of light).

Encourage the children to look for evidence of sound: the emergency service vehicles and the fire. It may be useful to ask them to be silent for a moment, then close their eyes and listen carefully for what they can hear in the classroom. Then ask: *How would it sound if you were in the picture?*

To explore the content of the poster as it relates to the work in this topic, it may be useful to ask the children the following questions:

◆ *Which things can you see that make their own light and help us to see?*

◆ *When do we use this light?* (The sun by day, the streetlights at night.)

◆ *When is it not used?* (The streetlights are not used during the day.)

◆ *When is it not so bright?* (When the sun is obscured by clouds.)

◆ *Which things in the picture make a sound?* (Firemen shouting instructions, the sirens, the dog barking, the radio and so on.)

◆ *Why is... making a sound?* (For example, the firemen want to make people do as they are told.)

◆ *Which things make both light and sound?* (For example, the fire engine.)

◆ *Why does it make both?* (In this case, so that other drivers know where it is and can get out of its way quickly.)

◆ *Which things in the picture help us to see better?* (Spectacles on the two adults in the car, mirrors to help the driver see behind the car.)

WHERE DOES LIGHT COME FROM?

GROUP SIZE AND ORGANIZATION
Whole class.
DURATION
20 minutes.
LEARNING OBJECTIVE
To learn that only certain kinds of objects emit (give out) their own light.

YOU WILL NEED
The 'car' poster, some small pieces of card and Blu-Tack, a torch, a candle, a small desk lamp, a flip chart, a marker pen.

WHAT TO DO
Before the class arrive, position the torch, candle and desk lamp around the room so that they are all visible (in different parts of the room).

Look at the 'car' poster with the children. Ask them to identify any objects in the picture that make their own light. They may suggest the sun, the fire, the lights of the vehicles, the street lights (if they were turned on). To help the children eliminate objects that have already been mentioned, cover each one with a piece of card (using Blu-Tack) and record it on the flip chart.

If a child suggests an object that does not emit its own light, such as a mirror, ask: *Could you use this object to help you see inside a dark cave? Could it help you to be seen at night where there are no street lights?* In this way, the child is not put off answering questions; and the discussion will lead into the next activity, where the children have to sort a range of objects into those that do and do not emit their own light.

Remind the children that objects that give off their own light are called *sources of light*. When all the appropriate objects on the poster have been covered up, ask the children to identify objects in the classroom – or objects that can be seen from the classroom – that can emit their own light. The children should be able to identify light sources such as the sun and the ceiling lights, as well as your three 'planted' items.

ASSESSMENT
Note those children who have assimilated the new vocabulary: *emit, source*. Note those who can identify the light sources in their environment.

IDEAS FOR DIFFERENTIATION
More able children could also be told that light is a form of energy; to make light, other types of energy (such as electrical energy) are converted into light energy. Ask them to identify where the light sources in the room (or on the poster) get their energy from.

LIGHT SOURCES

GROUP SIZE AND ORGANIZATION
Individuals or small groups.
DURATION
30 minutes.
LEARNING OBJECTIVE
To reinforce the distinction between objects that give out their own light (light sources) and other objects.

YOU WILL NEED
Photocopiable page 7, blank paper, scissors, adhesive, writing materials.
WHAT TO DO
Remind the children about how to identify light sources – for example, by considering *Will this object help me to see in dark places?*

Give each child a copy of photocopiable page 7. Tell the children that some of the objects on the sheet give out their own light and others do not. Ask them to cut out the pictures carefully, and then sort them into sources and non-sources of light. When they believe they have sorted the objects correctly, they can stick them onto two separate sheets of paper with appropriate labels.

Discuss the children's answers. The light sources are: sun, torch, candle with flame, television. If necessary, explain that the moon reflects the sun's light but emits no light of its own. The electricity from a battery can be used to make light (in a bulb), but the battery itself is not a light source.

ASSESSMENT
Note which children can sort the objects correctly and label one sheet using a suitable description such as the word 'sources'.

IDEAS FOR DIFFERENTIATION
More able children could be asked to think of and write down more sources of light.

IDEAS FOR DISPLAY
The correctly completed photocopiable sheets could be displayed as factsheets for reference. The children could work together to make a collage of different light sources cut from catalogues, magazines and newspapers.

LIGHT DETECTORS

GROUP SIZE AND ORGANIZATION
Whole class.
DURATION
30 minutes.
LEARNING OBJECTIVE
To learn how our eyes detect light in order for us to see.

YOU WILL NEED
An overhead projector (OHP) and screen, a pinhole camera (see Figure 1), photocopiable page 8 prepared as an overhead projector transparency (OHT), photocopiable pages 8 and 9, a convex lens (perhaps from a pair of glasses made to correct long sight).

WHAT TO DO
Show the children a 'black box' made up as shown in Figure 1. Tell them that this is going to be a model of the eye called a 'pinhole camera'. It may not look like an eye, but it tells us a lot about how our eyes work.

Using a pin, make a hole about 1mm wide in the front cover of the box. Ask the children to look at each other in pairs: can they see the part of the eye

that could be the same as the pinhole you have made in the box? The children may be able to tell you that it is the 'black bit in the middle'. Tell them that this part of the eye is the **pupil**, which allows the light into the eye – like the pinhole in the camera. Show the children the OHT of the human eye. Attach the label for the pupil (cut from photocopiable page 9) to the transparency in the correct place (or reveal a label that has been put there in advance).

Can the children say what happens to the light once it has gone into the camera or the eye? In the camera, the light travels through the inside of the box to hit the screen at the back. If the pinhole is now pointed at a bright light source such as the window or the image on the OHP screen, a very small image of the light source will appear on the translucent screen at the back of the camera.

Tell the children that there is a part at the back of the human eye, called the **retina**, which is like the screen. The retina is made of light-sensitive cells which transmit messages to your brain about the incoming light; these messages tell you what you have seen. The label for the retina can now be added to the OHT of the eye.

The image on the screen of the pinhole camera may be very dim. Can the children think of a way to make it brighter? They may suggest making a larger hole, so that more light can enter the camera. Our eyes can also change to allow in more or less light.

Ask the pairs to look at each other again. One child in each pair should close his/her eyes for 30 seconds, then open them; his/her partner should look carefully at the first child's pupils when the eyes open. What do they see? The pupils are large when the eyes are first opened, but shrink after a split second so that the right amount of light goes into the eye.

Using a pencil, increase the size of the pinhole slowly. **Do not** make a large hole straight away. Show the children how the image on the screen is getting brighter – but what else is happening to it? As the hole becomes larger the image becomes blurred, because the light rays striking the screen are coming along many different paths. To sharpen this image, we need a **lens** to make the light strike the screen in the correct place.

Place a convex lens in front of the enlarged pinhole and move it back and forth until a sharp image is obtained. The label for the lens can now be added to the OHT. Explain that we cannot see the lens in the eye, because it is **transparent** (clear). Explain also that the lens in the human eye cannot move backwards and forwards, so the surrounding muscles stretch it or let it relax, making it thinner or thicker, so that we can form a clear image of whatever we are looking at.

The other labels can now be placed on the OHT: the cornea (the clear coating across the eye) and the iris (the coloured part of the eye).

The children can now work individually with copies of photocopiable pages 8 and 9. They should cut out the labels from page 9 and place them on the eye diagram on page 8, then take another copy of page 9 and write down under each label what **function** (job) that part of the eye has.

ASSESSMENT
Note which children can label the parts of the eye correctly, and can explain (on photocopiable page 9) how these parts work together to enable us to see.

IDEAS FOR DIFFERENTIATION
Less confident pupils could label the parts of the eye without trying to explain their functions.

IDEAS FOR DISPLAY
Project the OHT used in the activity onto a display space on the wall, and trace around the eye diagram. The children can add the labels as appropriate.

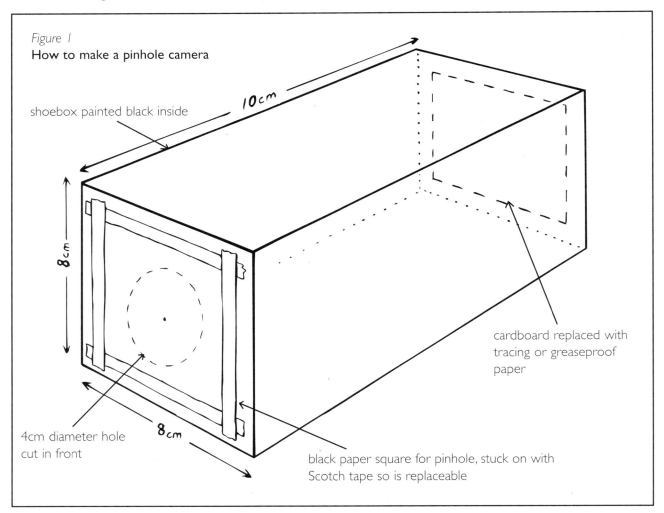

Figure 1
How to make a pinhole camera

shoebox painted black inside

10cm

8cm

8cm

cardboard replaced with tracing or greaseproof paper

4cm diameter hole cut in front

black paper square for pinhole, stuck on with Scotch tape so is replaceable

Light source or not?

◆ Cut out the pictures below and sort them into two groups: objects that give out their own light (light sources) and objects that do not give out their own light.

SOURCES AND DETECTORS

Name ——————————————— Date ———————————

Our eyes (1)

LIGHT AND SOUND

Name ——————————————— Date ———————————————

Our eyes (2)

◆ Cut out the six labels and stick them in the correct places on the eye diagram.

◆ On another copy of this sheet, write down the function of each part of the eye in the box under its name.

lens	pupil	retina
iris	cornea	optic nerve

The lens...

The pupil...

The retina...

The iris...

The cornea...

The optic nerve...

CAN I SEE THROUGH IT?

GROUP SIZE AND ORGANIZATION
Whole class.
DURATION
20 minutes.
LEARNING OBJECTIVE
To be able to identify different optical properties (transparent, opaque, translucent, coloured, colourless) and use them to classify materials.

YOU WILL NEED
The 'car' poster, 'flash cards' with photocopied light vocabulary from the back of the poster.

WHAT TO DO
Ask the children to look at the poster. What objects or materials can they see on the poster that are completely see-through? They should be able to identify various windows, for example in the car, shop and house fronts. They may also spot the covers on the streetlights; the lenses of the front passenger's spectacles or glasses; and the water from the hose. Tell the children that these are all made of clear glass (or plastic), which is a **transparent** material. Show them this word, on a 'flash card'. Ask them to spell it out and then tell you what it means.

Now ask the children to look at the poster again and find objects that are not at all see-through. There are many of these: walls, the road surface, the car seats and so on. Tell the children that these materials are **opaque**. Show them this word on a 'flash card'; ask the children to spell it out and tell you what it means.

Now ask the children to look at the poster again

and find objects that change the colour of light passing through them. It may be helpful to tell the children that all the lights on a vehicle are bulbs that give out white light. The children may identify the covers on the lights on the top of the fire engine and the police car; the indicator lights on a car; the covers on the traffic lights; and the sunglasses worn by the car driver. Ask the children whether these objects are transparent or opaque. Explain that they are in fact **translucent**: light will pass through them, but it is weakened and made fuzzy or blurred. These objects can also be classified as **coloured**, as can the opaque objects.

Finally, the objects that are **colourless** should be identified. Examples in the picture are glass (windows) and water. Colourless objects do not change the appearance of light passing through them.

The flash cards can be used in a later session to revise the spellings and meanings of these words (and other light words) with the class.

ASSESSMENT
Note which children can identify materials with the appropriate properties. (**NB** Make sure that the children do not confuse objects with their properties.) Note which children can spell the words on the flash cards, and can tell you clearly what they mean.

IDEAS FOR DIFFERENTIATION
With less confident children, leave out the discussion of 'translucent' materials. Use 'clear' and 'not clear' in place of 'transparent' and 'opaque'.

THE BUILDER'S YARD

GROUP SIZE AND ORGANIZATION
Small groups or individuals.
DURATION
30 to 40 minutes.
LEARNING OBJECTIVE
To be able to classify materials by their optical properties.

YOU WILL NEED
Photocopiable page 14, blank paper, writing materials, examples of some of the objects on the photocopiable sheet (such as wood, brick, clear plastic and frosted glass).

NB If you are using glass, cover up the edges with tape and only allow the children to handle it under close supervision.

EXIT

KRAKEN SEA MONSTER

SHADOWS

WHAT TO DO

Give the children a copy each of photocopiable page 14. Tell them that they have to sort the materials on the sheet – first into coloured and colourless objects, then into transparent, translucent and opaque objects. They can use the real materials provided to help them think about the problem. When they have sorted the materials in these two ways, they can use blank paper to show the data in the form of a table.

ASSESSMENT

Note which children classify the materials correctly. Glass, plastic sheeting and water are transparent; frosted glass is translucent; all of these are colourless. Brick, stone, wood, concrete, sand and metals are opaque and coloured.

IDEAS FOR DIFFERENTIATION

Less confident children may like to cut out the pictures on photocopiable page 14 and stick the pictures down in groups on a large sheet of paper. If a group of children use two or more copies of photocopiable page 14, they can still do both classifications.

More able children may try to group the materials in other ways after they have completed the task set. For example, they could classify the materials as natural and manufactured, or by the property of the material that makes it useful for the job it does in a particular object (for example: glass is transparent, so a glass window can let daylight into a building and allow people inside to look out).

IDEAS FOR DISPLAY

'Flash cards' with the words from the back of the poster could be pinned to the noticeboard alongside definitions of these words, with drawings of suitable objects placed around them in a collage.

MAKING SHADOWS

GROUP SIZE AND ORGANIZATION
Whole class.
DURATION
30 minutes.
LEARNING OBJECTIVE
To understand that opaque objects cast shadows when placed in front of a bright light source.

YOU WILL NEED

A bright source of light (such as an OHP or a desk lamp), a screen, a tennis ball, a ping-pong ball, pieces of card of various sizes, a piece of clear plastic, pencils, adhesive tape.

WHAT TO DO

Ask the children: *Do you know what a shadow is?* They may be able to tell you that a shadow is an area of darkness formed when an object blocks the light from a source. Use the following simple demonstrations to explore the nature of shadows with the class.

Demonstration 1

Show the children a piece of card and a piece of clear plastic. Ask them which they think will cast a shadow and which will not. Can they tell you which object is transparent and which is opaque?

Turn on the light source and hold both objects in between the light and the screen. Can the children say why there is no shadow with the plastic sheet? This will help to reinforce the idea that light passes through transparent materials.

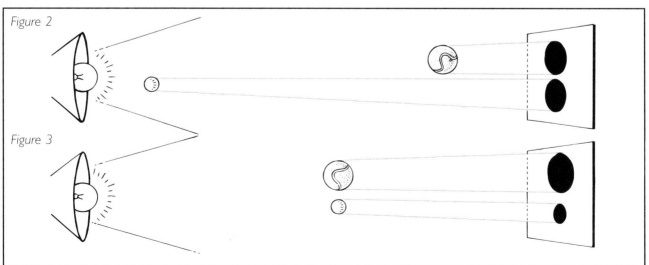

Figure 2

Figure 3

Demonstration 2

Hold the two balls about halfway between the light source and the screen, so that they cast shadows on the screen. Ask the children to say how the two shadows are different. They should observe that the shadow from the tennis ball is larger. (See Figure 2.) Can they explain why?

Ask a child to hold the tennis ball in place. Move the ping-pong ball towards the light source until the two shadows are the same size. Can the children explain this effect? Return the ping-pong ball to its original position. Now hold the ping-pong ball in place and move the tennis ball towards the screen until the two shadows are the same size. (See Figure 3.) Can the children explain this effect?

In this demonstration, the size of the shadow is related to the amount of light that the ball is able to block. Nearer the light source, more of the light can be obscured. This shows that light travels in straight lines.

Demonstration 3

Mount a square piece of card (approx. side length 10cm) on a pencil. Hold this between the light source and the screen so that a sharply defined shadow can be seen. Slowly turn the pencil until the face of the card is sideways-on to the light source. (See Figure 4.) How does the appearance of the shadow change? Can the children explain why?

The reason for the change in the shadow is the same as in Demonstration 2: the larger the object, the larger the shadow. Here, we are changing how much surface area is facing the light and thus blocking it: the greater the angle between the light and the object, the smaller the shadow.

This is the reason why a shadow cast in daylight changes during the day. As the Earth rotates on its axis, the angle which an object on the Earth's surface presents to the sun changes.

ASSESSMENT

Note which children can explain the changes in the appearance of the shadows in terms of the relative amount of light blocked by the objects.

IDEAS FOR DIFFERENTIATION

A group of more able children could make a shadow clock using a large piece of paper and a stick, as follows. Place the paper on the ground in an area of the school playground that is sunny all day and can be clearly marked (using calf marks or tape) if the paper has to be brought in during break or lunchtime. Hold the paper in place with heavy objects. Place the stick on the front edge of the paper and keep it standing with a block of Plasticine, so that it casts a shadow over the paper. Draw a straight line where the shadow lies, to mark its length and position. Write along the line the time it was drawn. Draw a new line at regular intervals during the day.

IDEAS FOR DISPLAY

The completed shadow clock (see above) can be displayed in the classroom, with a description of how the shadow changes its size and position depending on the stick's angle to the sun.

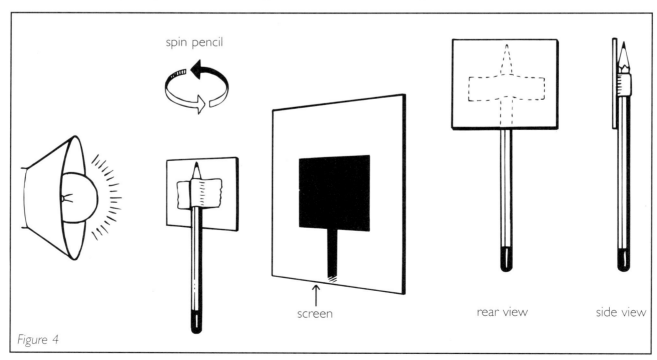

Figure 4

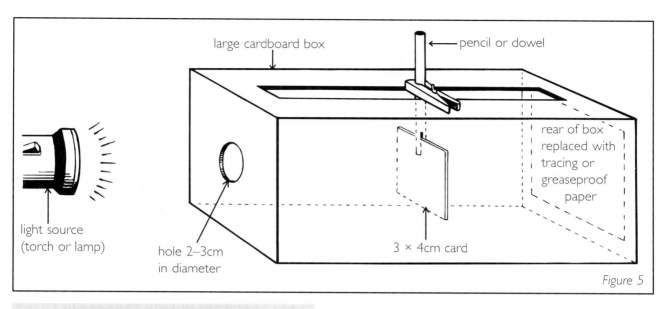

large cardboard box

pencil or dowel

rear of box replaced with tracing or greaseproof paper

light source (torch or lamp)

hole 2–3cm in diameter

3 × 4cm card

Figure 5

INVESTIGATING SHADOWS

GROUP SIZE AND ORGANIZATION
Small groups.
DURATION
40 to 60 minutes.
LEARNING OBJECTIVES
To learn how to predict the possible outcomes of experiments. To practise manipulating apparatus in order to test predictions. To record the results of investigations. To understand how the size of a shadow is related to the relative positions of the object, light source and screen.

YOU WILL NEED
Photocopiable page 15, a torch, a shoe box, a sheet of card (3cm × 4cm), adhesive tape; two rulers, lollipop sticks or pencils.

WHAT TO DO
Organise the class into small groups and give each group a copy of photocopiable page 15. Tell them that they are going to investigate how the appearance of a shadow changes when the distance between the light and the object changes.

Set up an 'Investigating shadows' workstation for the children to use (see Figure 5) before they start the investigation. Photocopiable page 15 will guide them through the investigation by providing leading questions and a table in which they can record their results. Let each group in turn carry out the experiment under your supervision.

The children should first predict how the shadow will appear when the object is close to the light source, and then how it will appear when the object is further away from the light source. They should then turn on the light and place the object in the box. As the box has a built-in screen and a scale to measure the position of the object, the children can position the object accurately and use a ruler to measure the width of the shadow cast.

Working together, the children in each group should fill in the results table and decide whether their results support their prediction.

ASSESSMENT
Note which groups:
◆ make a sensible prediction;
◆ manipulate the apparatus with care in order to test their prediction;
◆ record their results with care and accuracy.

IDEAS FOR DIFFERENTIATION
More able children could be asked to write out their predictions in more detail, including the reasons for their predictions. They could also design their own results table and write a brief (one-sentence) conclusion to say what they have found out from the experiment.

Children who find this activity difficult to grasp could make fewer readings, or simply judge whether the shadows made are 'small', 'medium' or 'large'.

IDEAS FOR DISPLAY
Display the test station, or a drawing of it, together with the children's records of their investigation on photocopiable page 15.

Name _____   Date _____

Sorting out the builder's yard

◆ Sort these materials into two kinds: **coloured** (mark **X** with a coloured pen) and **colourless** (mark **X** with a black pen).

◆ Now sort the same materials into three kinds: **transparent** (mark **T1**), **translucent** (mark **T2**) and **opaque** (mark **O**).

◆ Use a blank sheet of paper to record your results in a table.

LIGHT AND SOUND

SHADOWS

Name ——————————————— Date ———————————————

Investigating shadows

Prediction (your guess)

When the object is nearer the torch, the shadow will be…

When the object is further from the torch, the shadow will be…

Results (what you have measured)

Distance from torch to card (cm)	Height of shadow (cm)

PHOTOCOPIABLE

RESOURCE
BANK

SEEING AND REFLECTION

SEEING THE LIGHT

GROUP SIZE AND ORGANIZATION
Whole class sitting in a semicircle, facing the teacher.
DURATION
20 minutes.
LEARNING OBJECTIVE
To learn that light from a source travels into our eyes both directly and by the reflection of scattered light from non-luminous objects (which do not give out their own light).

YOU WILL NEED
The 'car' poster, a view out of the classroom window.

WHAT TO DO
Ask the children to look first at the 'car' poster and then at the view from the window; each time, ask them to identify objects that give out their own light. Ask questions about how they see things, such as:
◆ *Where does the light from these sources go?* (In all directions, but some will enter our eyes.)
◆ *What happens when the light enters your eye?* (It is detected by the retina and decoded as a 'picture' by the brain.)
◆ *What happens when it hits another object, for example a tree?* (Some of the light is scattered or reflected from the object.)
◆ *Where does the light go to from the tree?* (It is scattered in all directions; some of it enters our eyes.)
◆ *What happens to the light reflected from the tree that goes into your eye?* (As before, the light is detected by the retina and decoded into an image of a tree.)
Discuss a range of light sources and objects in this way.

IDEAS FOR DIFFERENTIATION
More able children can be led, through questioning, to consider how we see coloured light:
◆ *What colour of light bounces off this object?* (For example, when white light from the sun strikes a red post-box, only red light is reflected; when white light strikes a leaf, only green light is reflected.)

WHERE DOES LIGHT GO?

GROUP SIZE AND ORGANIZATION
Whole class.
DURATION
15 minutes.
LEARNING OBJECTIVES
To reinforce the knowledge that when a non-luminous object is seen, light travels from a source to the object and then to the eye. To develop predicting skills for science investigation.

YOU WILL NEED
A torch or bicycle light, a room that can be darkened.

WHAT TO DO
Ask the children to predict which objects in the room might still be visible if the room were almost dark (as if it were night-time). Ask: *Why have you chosen these objects?* Now darken the room. Were the predictions for the more visible items correct? (Lighter or more reflective materials should be more visible.)
Now ask: *What could you use to help you see where you were going if there were no lights in the room or on the street outside?* Produce the torch – a portable light source! Ask the children which way they would point the torch to look at an object: *Towards your eyes?* (Do **not** try this!) *Towards the floor? Towards the object?*
Ask them where the light goes. Can they describe the whole journey of the light beam? (For example: the light ray travels from the torch to the hamster; some light is reflected or scattered by the hamster into our eyes, thus enabling us to see the hamster.)

IDEAS FOR DIFFERENTIATION
Ask more able children to explain why some objects appear brighter than others in dim light. (The reason is that more light is reflected, rather than being scattered or absorbed, by the surface of the object.)

SEEING AND REFLECTION

FOLLOWING THE LIGHT

GROUP SIZE AND ORGANIZATION
Individuals or small groups.
DURATION
About 20 minutes.
LEARNING OBJECTIVE
To follow the path of light from a source to the observer's eye.

YOU WILL NEED
Photocopiable page 19, pencils, rulers.

WHAT TO DO
Give out copies of photocopiable page 19. Ask the children to draw arrows to show which way the light is travelling in each picture. The arrows should be drawn as straight lines, and the direction of the light should be clearly marked. In some cases, the light is coming from different places in the picture; the children must show all the different possible paths.

ASSESSMENT
Note whether the children consistently draw the correct path from source to eye, via another object where appropriate. Figure 6 shows an example.

IDEAS FOR DIFFERENTIATION
More able children could draw their own light paths for objects at home or school, extending the work done on photocopiable page 19.

IDEAS FOR DISPLAY
Large-scale diagrams, using pieces of string to represent the light beams passing between sources and detectors, can be mounted on the wall. A central light source can be painted in the middle of a group of diagrams to show, for example, the sun lighting up trees and buildings which are 'seen' by people and video cameras.

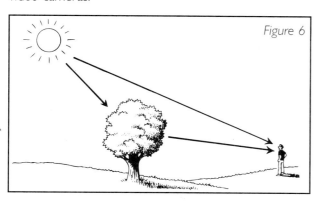

Figure 6

REFLECTED LIGHT

GROUP SIZE AND ORGANIZATION
Small groups of about four children.
DURATION
About 45–60 minutes.
LEARNING OBJECTIVES
To find out, through investigation, which materials reflect light best and thus have a better chance of being seen in 'the dark'. To practise observing and recording experimental results, and drawing conclusions from them.

YOU WILL NEED
A small light source (such as a torch or bicycle light), a shoe box, cardboard tubes, photocopiable page 20, a labelled selection of reflective and dull materials. Examples of good reflective materials include fluorescent marker pens, reflectors from bicycles, mirrors and Scotchlite™ tape on children's jackets.

WHAT TO DO
Tell the children that they are going to investigate what types of materials are best at reflecting light. They will need to think carefully about how this can be done **fairly** – that is, so that the only factor that changes during the experiment is the material being tested. The children need to consider how they will ensure that a controlled amount of light hits the material, and that the amount of light coming back from the material is not affected by the light in the room.

Following discussion, give out copies of photocopiable page 20; the children can look at the 'Reflection test station' to see whether it conforms to their criteria. Set up the reflection test station as shown on page 20. The children can place each material in the box on the mounting card, shine the light down Tube 1 and observe any reflected light through Tube 2. Each child can then record his or her observations in the table on page 20.

The results should show that the lighter-coloured, smoother and more 'metallic' materials are the better reflectors. This is due to the more regular reflection of the incident light: the light is less scattered, and thus more light travels towards our eyes. These would be the best materials to wear at night in order to be seen.

ASSESSMENT
Note which children are able to manipulate the materials effectively, record the results clearly, and complete the two sentences on the sheet correctly.

SEEING AND REFLECTION

IDEAS FOR DIFFERENTIATION
Less able pupils could concentrate on three or four strongly contrasting materials.

IDEAS FOR DISPLAY
Ask the children to design clothes for children going home in the dark, or for people who work in the dark and have to be seen (for example, emergency services). They could also develop ideas about how we could use camouflage to hide at night. Child-sized collages of these designs could be compiled.

If time permits, a whole-body demonstration can be made. Select two children to stand in front of the rest of the class. Label them as A and B. They should face each other, feet shoulder-width apart, hands by their sides, sideways-on to the rest of the class. A places left hand on head; B copies the movement as a 'mirror image'. A touches nose with first finger of right hand; B copies. Now move both children so that they face the class. What can the class observe? They should point out that B has **right** hand on head and is touching nose with **left** hand.

MIRRORS

GROUP SIZE AND ORGANIZATION
Whole class, then pairs or small groups.
DURATION
10 minutes, then 20–30 minutes.
LEARNING OBJECTIVES
To learn that mirrors reflect light without scattering and give a clear image of what is in front of them. To learn that images in a mirror are 'laterally inverted': the left-hand side of the object appears to be on the right, and vice versa.

YOU WILL NEED
The 'car' poster, a small hand-held mirror, a plastic mirror for each child, writing materials.

WHAT TO DO
Look at the 'car' poster with the children. Ask them: *Can you see any mirrors? What can you see in these mirrors?* (The view behind the car.) *What happens to things when they are looked at in a mirror?* (The left and right sides are reversed; letters appear 'backwards'.)

Using a hand-held mirror, discuss the path that the light takes in order for it to be seen by our eyes. By now, the children should be able to say that we see an object when the light goes from the source to the object and is reflected into our eyes. When we see an object in a mirror, the light reflected from the object is reflected again by the mirror into our eyes.

Now ask the children to sit opposite each other in pairs. Child 1 should close the left eye, and Child 2 should draw Child 1's face with the eye shut. They should then swap roles, so that Child 1 draws Child 2. Finally, both children should draw themselves when looking in a mirror with the left eye closed. It helps if each child holds the mirror while the other draws. The two drawings made by each child can be compared.

RIGHT WAY ROUND

GROUP SIZE AND ORGANIZATION
Small groups.
DURATION
15 minutes, then 40 minutes.
LEARNING OBJECTIVES
To see how reflection affects the letters of the alphabet, and how this has implications for the emergency services.

YOU WILL NEED
For each group: photocopiable page 21, a pencil, a small plastic mirror.

WHAT TO DO
Organize the children into small groups. Give each group a copy of photocopiable page 21 and a mirror. Tell them to place the mirror next to each letter and compare the letter on the page with its reflection in the mirror. They should then put a tick next to each letter that looks *exactly* the same as its reflection. The final part of the sheet gives the children the opportunity to practise 'mirror writing' by making signs for the emergency services that could be read in the mirror of a car. They can use mirrors to test each other's signs.

ASSESSMENT
Note which children correctly identify those letters that can undergo lateral inversion without changing their appearance.

IDEAS FOR DISPLAY
The children can cut out letter shapes from coloured paper to display the 'normal' and 'reflected' view of the words on emergency service vehicles (or of the whole alphabet).

Name _____   Date _____

Following the light

♦ Draw an arrow to show the path of a light beam from a light source to an object, and then to the eye of someone looking at that object.

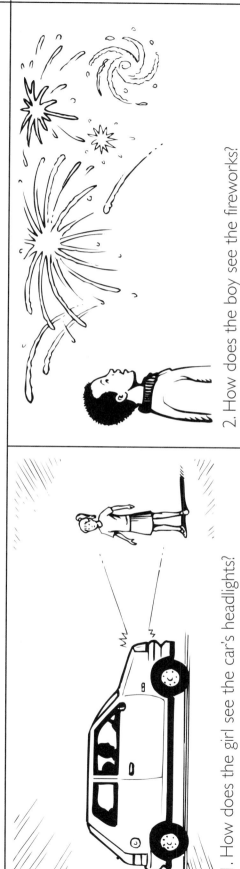

2. How does the boy see the fireworks?

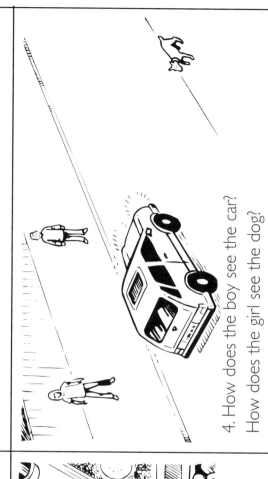

4. How does the boy see the car?
How does the girl see the dog?

1. How does the girl see the car's headlights?

3. How do the audience see the band?

SEEING AND REFLECTION

Name _____   Date _____

Reflection test station

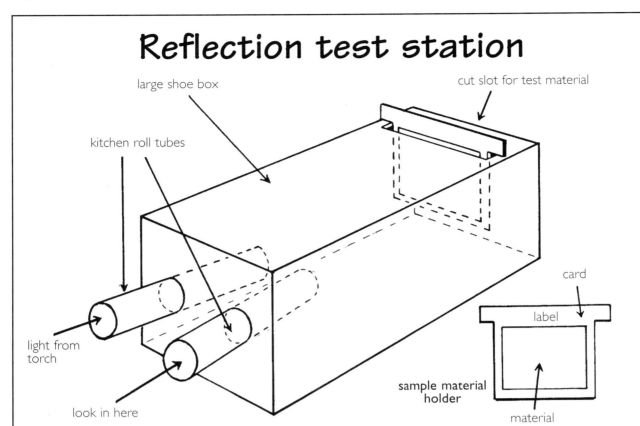

large shoe box

kitchen roll tubes

cut slot for test material

light from torch

look in here

card

label

sample material holder

material

Reflected light

Material	Reflects a lot of light	Reflects very little/no light

The best materials to wear at night if you want to be seen in the dark are:

The best materials to wear at night if you do **not** want to be seen in the dark are:

SEEING AND REFLECTION

Name ———————————————————   Date ———————————————

Coded words

◆ Put a tick (✓) next to the letters that look **the same** when you read them in a mirror.

A	B	C	D	E	F
G	H	I	J	K	L
M	N	O	P	Q	R
S	T	U	V	W	X
Y	Z				

◆ Write down which letters look the same when you look at them in a mirror.

◆ Try to write the words FIRE, POLICE and AMBULANCE so that they will look right when they are read in a mirror.

FIRE

POLICE

AMBULANCE

PHOTOCOPIABLE
RESOURCE
BANK

MAKING SOUNDS

HOW WE MAKE SOUNDS

GROUP SIZE AND ORGANIZATION
Whole class.
DURATION
30 minutes.
LEARNING OBJECTIVE
To learn that sounds are made when objects vibrate. To learn about how the different sounds of the human voice are made.

YOU WILL NEED
The 'car' poster.

WHAT TO DO
Show the children the 'car' poster. Ask them to identify objects that make sounds. They may suggest the sirens of the emergency service vehicles, the fire, people shouting, the dog barking and the radio in the car.

Tell the children that they are going to look at how they make sounds when they speak. Ask them simply to open their mouths – note that this makes no sound. Now ask them to place their fingertips gently on the front of the neck (the throat), near the base, then say *Aarrgghh!* Can they feel anything? They should feel a slight vibration, which is the source of the sound. Explain that air from the lungs is coming through that part of the throat to make the vibration happen.

Now ask the children to make the *Aarrgghh!* sound again, but to close their mouths as they do so. What can they hear? The sound changes, because the shape of the mouth makes a difference to how the air vibrates. The children could spend some time investigating how they can change the sound of *Aarrgghh!* just by changing the shape of the mouth.

Now ask the children to close their lips and hum. Can they find the vibration? They will find it in the throat as before, but there is no air escaping through the lips this time. Ask them to hum again; but this time, when they are humming, they should gently squeeze the nose. The humming stops, because the air is no longer allowed to move and so all the vibration stops. As a further demonstration, a few children could be asked to say their names to the class – once while holding their noses and once without. They should find that the consonants 'm' and 'n' are most affected.

This activity demonstrates that the sounds of the human voice come from the throat, but depend on the movement of air through the mouth and/or nose.

HOW MY VOICE WORKS

GROUP SIZE AND ORGANIZATION
Small groups or individuals.
DURATION
20 minutes.
LEARNING OBJECTIVE
To learn the positions of the organs we use for speaking. To reinforce knowledge of the paths that air takes when we speak.

YOU WILL NEED
Photocopiable page 25, scissors, adhesive.

WHAT TO DO
Give out one copy per child (or group) of photocopiable page 25. Tell the children that they are going to label the parts of the body that help them to speak. They need to cut out the labels at the bottom of the sheet and put them in the correct places on the diagram of the upper body.

Next, the children have to match the organs to the phrases that describe their functions in speech. They should cut the phrases from the bottom of the sheet and stick them (or copy them) next to the appropriate labels on the diagram.

ASSESSMENT
Note which children label the body parts correctly and identify their roles in making speech. The answers are as follows. The air supply is held in the lungs. The windpipe takes the air to and from the lungs through the voice box. The voice box makes the vibrations. The mouth contains the tongue and has lips to help you make different sounds. The nose is another path for air to travel in and out through when we breathe and speak, and helps with making different sounds.

IDEAS FOR DIFFERENTIATION
Giving the children the first letter of each label on the diagram will help less able pupils to find the correct word more easily. With the function labels, clues could be given such as the number of letters in the matching word (for example, a clue for 'throat' could be '6 letters' or '_ _ _ _ _ _').

IDEAS FOR DISPLAY
Photocopiable page 25 could be copied onto an OHT to allow the projection of the upper body diagram onto the noticeboard for children to draw around and label.

RESOURCE
BANK

MAKING SOUNDS

MUSICAL INSTRUMENTS

GROUP SIZE AND ORGANIZATION
Whole class.
DURATION
20 minutes.
LEARNING OBJECTIVE
To learn that part of a musical instrument must be vibrating in order for the instrument to make a sound. To learn how these vibrations can be changed in order to make a different sound.

YOU WILL NEED
Real musical instruments (such as a violin, recorder, tambourine or drum) and/or basic home-made instruments (such as an elastic-band guitar, milk-bottle flute or paper straw 'oboe' – see Figure 7). Examples of unfamiliar world instruments would be interesting to investigate.

WHAT TO DO
Show an instrument to the children, and ask them how you could use it to make a sound. The children's likely answers will depend on the chosen instrument; but give any valid answer a try to see whether the instrument will play. Remind the children that to make a sound, there must be a vibration. Can they identify the vibrating part of the instrument?

In a stringed instrument, the vibration of the strings makes the sound. In a percussion instrument, the struck surface vibrates. In a wind instrument, the vibrating part is the air travelling through (though the way in which the air is made to vibrate can vary – for example, a reed in an oboe, lips playing a trumpet).

ASSESSMENT
Note which children make reasonable suggestions for how to play each instrument, and can identify the vibrating parts.

IDEAS FOR DISPLAY
See 'Pitch and loudness' on page 24.

SORTING INSTRUMENTS

GROUP SIZE AND ORGANIZATION
Small groups.
DURATION
30 minutes.
LEARNING OBJECTIVE
To learn how to classify instruments by the way they are played or the part of the instrument that vibrates.

YOU WILL NEED
Photocopiable page 26, scissors, adhesive, A4 paper.

WHAT TO DO
Give each group a copy of photocopiable page 26. Tell the children that the ten musical instruments on the sheet are played in three different ways: by striking, by blowing or by plucking and scraping. Their task is to sort the instruments into the correct groups and to write labels saying which part of each instrument is vibrating. They can do this by cutting out the pictures and then working together to place them on A4 paper before sticking them down and labelling them.

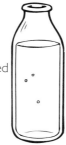  

Figure 7

Elastic band guitar
Open box (cardboard or plastic) with various elastic bands.
To play: pluck the elastic bands.

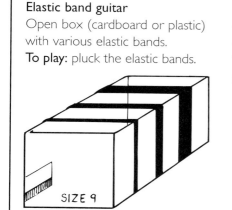

Milk bottle flute or drum
Bottles (preferably glass) filled with different amounts of water (could be coloured).
To play: blow across top of bottle or hit with a pencil.

Paper straw oboe
Flatten last 1cm of straw.
Cut to form a 'V' shape.
To play: put flattened end of straw approx. 2cm into mouth and blow through it.

MAKING SOUNDS

ASSESSMENT

Note which groups can sort the musical instruments correctly and identify the vibrating part of each instrument. The answers are:

◆ Striking – cymbal (metal disc vibrates), drum (skin vibrates), piano (strings vibrate), claves (sticks vibrate).

◆ Blowing – trumpet (lips vibrate), recorder (air vibrates), clarinet (reed vibrates).

◆ Plucking and scraping – guitar (strings and air inside guitar vibrate), violin (strings and air inside violin vibrate), cello (strings and air inside cello vibrate).

IDEAS FOR DISPLAY

An enlarged copy of photocopiable page 26 could be cut up, and the pictures mounted along with the children's drawings of musical instruments. (They could invent new instruments and say how these are played.)

MAKING MUSIC

GROUP SIZE AND ORGANIZATION
Whole class.
DURATION
20 minutes.
LEARNING OBJECTIVE
To learn that a musical instrument can make different sounds if the way it vibrates (or the way the air within it vibrates) changes.

YOU WILL NEED

See 'Musical instruments', page 23.

WHAT TO DO

Tell the children that a tune is made up from different notes, and that musical instruments can be adjusted to make many different sounds. Choose an instrument and play a high note and a low note on it. Can they hear the difference? Ask them which note was higher. **Do not** show them how the note was changed, since they will investigate this in the next activity.

◆ To change the note on a stringed instrument: use thinner or thicker strings or elastic bands, change the tension, or change the length of the vibrating string.

◆ To change the note on a percussion instrument: change the size of the struck area, change the skin tension, or change the volume of air in the container.

◆ To change the note on a wind instrument: change the length of the instrument, or cover different holes.

PITCH AND LOUDNESS

GROUP SIZE AND ORGANIZATION
Small groups.
DURATION
45–60 minutes.
LEARNING OBJECTIVE
To investigate how the pitch and the loudness of a note can be changed.

YOU WILL NEED

A selection of real and/or home-made musical instruments: tuning forks, elastic-band guitars, milk-bottle flutes, paper-straw 'oboes', xylophones, drums, triangles, recorders and so on; photocopiable page 27.

WHAT TO DO

Arrange the instruments around the room. Tell the children that they must visit each instrument, filling in a form on the sheet each time. Give each group enough copies of photocopiable page 27 for them to do this. Tell them that they will have five minutes at each 'station' to examine and play the instrument, so that they can fill in all of the questions. All of their findings should be written down. They should not move on before they are told to, or a crowd may form around a popular instrument.

The results of the children's experiments should match the information given above (see 'Making music'). Explain that the **pitch** of a note (how high it is) depends on how quickly the instrument vibrates (the **frequency** of the sound). The **volume** of a sound depends on the size (or **amplitude**) of the vibrations.

ASSESSMENT

Note which groups examine the instruments carefully and fill in their answer sheets correctly. From their answers, note which children show a clear understanding of the difference between loudness and pitch.

IDEAS FOR DIFFERENTIATION

By working with an individual group, you could give additional guidance to less able children and help them with filling in the answer sheet.

IDEAS FOR DISPLAY

The children could go back to the display they made in 'Sorting instruments' (see page 23) and write an additional label to stick beside each instrument, saying how different notes could be obtained from it.

Name ———————————————— Date ————————————————

How my voice works

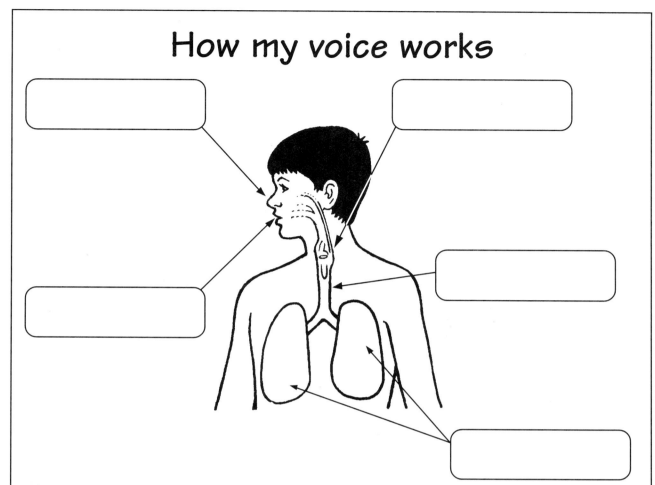

◆ Use these words to label your diagram:

lungs, windpipe, voice box, nose, mouth

◆ Put the correct sentences with the words to say
how each organ helps you to speak:

Contains the tongue and has lips to help you make different sounds.

Is another path for air to travel in and out through when you breathe
and speak, and helps with making different sounds.

Makes the sound vibrations.

Takes the air to and from the lungs through the voice box.

The air supply is held here.

Name _____   Date _____

Sorting musical instruments

◆ Sort these instruments into groups, using the way that each instrument is played.

trumpet

recorder

guitar

drum

cymbal

cello

clarinet

violin

claves

piano

MAKING SOUNDS

Name ——————————————— Date ———————————————

High and low, loud and quiet

◆ Fill out a form for each musical instrument you use.

Name of the instrument . . . .
How I play the instrument . . . .
How I make a high sound . . . .
How I make a low sound . . . .
How I make a loud sound . . . .
How I make a quiet sound . . . .

Name of the instrument . . . .
How I play the instrument . . . .
How I make a high sound . . . .
How I make a low sound . . . .
How I make a loud sound . . . .
How I make a quiet sound . . . .

Name of the instrument . . . .
How I play the instrument . . . .
How I make a high sound . . . .
How I make a low sound . . . .
How I make a loud sound . . . .
How I make a quiet sound . . . .

Name of the instrument . . . .
How I play the instrument . . . .
How I make a high sound . . . .
How I make a low sound . . . .
How I make a loud sound . . . .
How I make a quiet sound . . . .

PHOTOCOPIABLE
RESOURCE
BANK

HOW SOUND GETS TO YOU

GROUP SIZE AND ORGANIZATION
Whole class.
DURATION
20 minutes.
LEARNING OBJECTIVE
To learn how sound travels from a source to our ears. To learn how our ears work in order for us to hear.

YOU WILL NEED
The 'car' poster, an OHP, photocopiable page 31 copied onto an OHT.

WHAT TO DO
Look at the poster with the children. Ask them what sounds the people and things in the picture might be making. For each suggested sound, ask: *Does this sound have any meaning?* (For example, as a warning.) *What is needed to make the sound?* Remind them about vibration if necessary. *How would you detect the vibration?* They should be able to reply that they would detect it as a sound, using their ears.

When a sound is made, an object vibrates. This causes the air around it to vibrate, and the vibrations travel out into the surroundings. Some of these vibrations go into our ears.

Switch on the OHP to show the OHT of the ear. Ask the children to look at each other: which part of the ear can they see? (The **ear flap**, outer ear or pinna.) Label the ear flap on the OHT, and explain that it has a special shape to collect sound vibrations and direct them into the **ear canal** or middle ear. Label the ear canal on the OHT.

Once inside the ear, the vibrations strike the **eardrum** and make it vibrate. The eardrum is a tiny piece of skin that can be damaged by loud noises, because it is very sensitive to vibration. Label the eardrum.

Behind the eardrum is the **inner ear**, containing three small bones called the **hammer, anvil and stirrup** (because of their shapes). Their job is to increase the size of the vibration before passing on the vibration to the **cochlea**, a spiral tube. Inside the cochlea is some liquid that moves with the vibrations. Fine hairs detect movement in the liquid, and nerves connected to the hairs send a message to the brain telling you that you have heard something. Label the bones, cochlea and nerve.

HEAR ARE OUR EARS

GROUP SIZE AND ORGANIZATION
Small groups or individuals.
DURATION
30 minutes.
LEARNING OBJECTIVE
To reinforce knowledge of the parts of the ear and their roles in allowing us to hear.

YOU WILL NEED
Photocopiable page 31, scissors, adhesive, blank A4 paper, coloured pens or pencils.

WHAT TO DO
Give out one copy per child or group of photocopiable page 31. Explain to the children that they have to cut out the labels (giving the names and functions of different parts of the ear) and place them on the diagram, then colour-code each part and its two labels. (For example, the cochlea could be coloured in red and the labels given a red border.) The cut-out ear diagram and the labels should then be glued onto a sheet of A4 paper.

ASSESSMENT
Note which children label the parts of the ear correctly. The names and functions should be paired up as follows:
◆ Ear flap – the part of the ear you can see [on the outside].
◆ Nerve – [the auditory nerve] sends messages to the brain.
◆ Hammer, anvil and stirrup – three bones that increase the size of the vibrations.
◆ Ear-drum – a piece of skin [inside the ear] that detects vibrations.
◆ Cochlea – a coiled tube containing liquid.
◆ Ear canal – sends vibrations to the ear-drum.

IDEAS FOR DIFFERENTIATION
For less able children, clues to the labels could be written onto the diagram – for example, the first two letters of the name of each part of the ear. Label lines could also be drawn to help them identify the relevant parts of the ear.

IDEAS FOR DISPLAY

The labelled ear diagrams could be mounted and displayed on the classroom wall, perhaps around a larger diagram of the ear that has been drawn using the OHT from the previous activity.

NOISE ANNOYS

GROUP SIZE AND ORGANIZATION
Whole class, then small groups.
DURATION
20 minutes discussion, 45–60 minutes work for display.
LEARNING OBJECTIVE
To understand that noise in our environment disturbs others and can damage hearing.

YOU WILL NEED
The 'car' poster, colouring pens or pencils, paint or collage materials, poster paper.

WHAT TO DO
Look at the 'car' poster with the children. Can they name things in the picture that make pleasant, enjoyable sounds? They may suggest the car stereo, the personal stereo, birds in the trees, people talking. Can they name things on the poster that make a horrible noise, din or racket? They may suggest the car engine, the car stereo (parental choice of music!), the dog barking, the sirens on the emergency service vehicles.

Ask the children to think of some more examples of pleasant sounds and nasty noises. Now ask them to explain *why* they like or do not like a particular sound. Sounds that are generally agreed to be pleasant have clear and distinctive tones; and while we may not all agree on the best type of music, it is usually possible to tell the difference between 'music' and 'noise'. The notes in 'music' are ordered and in harmony (agreement). 'Noise' is a confused jumble of tones, formless and chaotic.

Ask the children how these different sounds make them feel. When they were small, they went to sleep listening to a gentle adult voice which made them feel relaxed; now, perhaps, they listen to music which makes them want to dance and sing or just to relax and dream. How does noise make them feel? They probably want it to stop or to go away; it may make them feel poorly, give them headaches or earache.

Ask: *Do you ever make noise that annoys other people? Do you think you should be more thoughtful?*

The children can now work in small groups to design a poster, either to advertise their favourite sounds or to announce that an unwelcome noise is banned.

IDEAS FOR DISPLAY
The children's 'favourite sounds' posters could be displayed in the school's music area; their 'anti-noise' posters could be displayed in a quiet area, such as the reading corner or the library.

REDUCING NOISE POLLUTION

GROUP SIZE AND ORGANIZATION
Small groups.
DURATION
30–45 minutes.
LEARNING OBJECTIVE
To learn how materials can be used to reduce the amount of noise passing through the environment. To practise prediction, planning, recording and drawing conclusions in science investigation.

YOU WILL NEED
A small battery-operated radio, cassette player or alarm clock; a box to fit this object in, with space around the side to add insulation materials; a range of insulation materials such as bubble wrap, various fabrics, shredded or scrunched-up paper, sponge foam and LEGO™ blocks; photocopiable page 32.

HEARING AND DISTANCE

WHAT TO DO

Ask the children to be silent and listen carefully. Can they hear other classes in the school, or sounds from outside? Tell them that they can hear these sounds because vibrations from sound source can pass through walls and windows. Explain that sounds can be **muffled** or prevented from moving around if certain materials are used to absorb the vibrations. For example, it would be hard for them to hear what you were saying if you put a hand over your mouth or had a scarf wrapped around your face.

Ask the children whether they have seen or used anything that makes noise less. Have they noticed what happens in a room when all the furniture is removed and the curtains taken down before the room is redecorated? It sounds 'echoey' because there are no soft materials to stop the sounds bouncing around. Soft materials help to **absorb** or 'soak up' the vibrations of sound.

Tell the children they are going to do an investigation in order to answer the question: *Which materials are best for reducing the amount of sound coming from a noisy object?* They should place the 'noisy object' (such as a portable radio) inside the box, then choose materials to put in the box in order to absorb the sound.

The children should be encouraged to plan the experiment as a **fair test** – that is, to make sure that only the sound-insulating material is changed during the test, while all the other factors in the experiment remain unchanged. For example, if a radio is used as the sound source, care must be taken not to change the volume at which the radio is playing. As far as possible, the same amount of each insulating material should be used. Also, they should set up a **control** situation as a basis for comparison – in this case, listening to the sound without any sound-absorbing materials in order to hear the initial volume level.

Give each group a copy of photocopiable page 32, which provides a guide to the investigation. The children should list the materials they are using, predict which will be the best sound insulator and give a reason for their choice. They should fill in the results table, judging the efficiency of each insulating material by giving the sound they can still hear a mark out of 10 (from 10 if the material has no effect down to 1 if they can only just hear it). Finally, they should record which materials they found to be the worst and best insulators.

ASSESSMENT

Note which children:
◆ can predict the outcome of an experiment;
◆ can carry out an experiment to test their prediction;
◆ show awareness of the need for a 'fair test';
◆ can record the results of an experiment;
◆ can draw logical and sensible conclusions from the results.

IDEAS FOR DIFFERENTIATION

More confident children should be encouraged to write their own format for the experiment, using photocopiable page 32 as a guide. They should include a plan, a prediction, a table of results and a conclusion.

For less confident children, restrict the number of materials to be tested to three: the control (no material) and two strongly contrasting insulation materials, such as sponge foam and LEGO™ blocks.

IDEAS FOR DISPLAY

The children could use their findings to design a 'chill-out' room in a disco where tired dancers could hold a conversation or take a rest, using insulation materials to stop the music interfering. These designs could be displayed as pictures or models.

RESOURCE
BANK

Name _____   Date _____

Hear are our ears

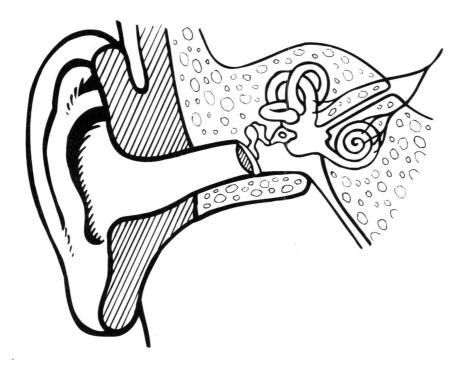

◆ Use the words and sentences below to name each part of the ear and say what its job is.

Ear flap
Nerve
Hammer, anvil and stirrup
Ear-drum
Cochlea
Ear canal

Sends vibrations to the ear-drum.
The part of the ear you can see.
A coiled tube containing liquid.
Three bones that increase the size of the vibrations.
A piece of skin that detects vibrations.
Sends messages to the brain.

Name _____   Date _____

Reducing noise pollution

The materials I will try putting in my box to stop the sound are:

. . . .

. . . .

The material I think will stop the most sound is:

I think this material will work best because:

. . . .

. . . .

. . . .

. . . .

Results

Material used in the box	Sound level (from 1 to 10)

What I have found out

The most sound came out of the box when I used:

The best material for stopping sound was: